BEAU PEEP

BY ROGER KETTLE & ANDREW CHRISTINE

AN EXPRESS BOOKS PUBLICATION

Printed by Eyre & Spittiswoode, Cosham, Hants. & co-ordinated by Roeder Print Services Ltd.

Welcome to book 9! On my left is Roger the writer, right? For you, Roger the writer is right on the right while Andrew the artist is left on the left, right? That's **your** left. Andrew is right by my side on the right from **my** side which is the right side to be on. So from right to left, it's Roger the writer, me and Andrew the artist, right? So march on in and enjoy my latest adventures – left, right, left, right . . .

THE ADVENTURES OF LEGIONNAIRE

BEAU PEEP

FROM **THE STAR**

"DEAR LEGIONNAIRE ON THE WALL, YOU ARE VERY HANDSOME."
1990

"I REALLY LIKE YOUR CUTE, LOP-SIDED SMILE"

I WONDER WHO SHE MEANS? IT COULD BE ANYONE.

WHAT?

D'YOU THINK SHE'S WATCHING?
WHO?
1992

THE WOMAN WHO'S SENDING US LETTERS!
PROBABLY.

I THINK I'LL SHOW HER MY BEST SIDE.

WELL, KEEP YOUR TROUSERS ON.

LOOK! ANOTHER LETTER FROM MY ADMIRER!
1993

THE POOR GIRL HAS SEEN MY FACE AND FALLEN IN LOVE— SIMPLE AS THAT!

SHE MUST BE.

READ OUT THE NEW LETTER FROM MY ADMIRER!
YOU WON'T LIKE IT.
1994

"I LOVE YOUR GLASSES AND YOUR LITTLE MOUSTACHE."

I'M SORRY, DENNIS. IT WOULD SEEM THAT, ALL ALONG, SHE MEANT—

TRYING TO MAKE ME JEALOUS, EH? DON'T FIGHT IT YOU FOOL!

AH, THERE YOU ARE!
1983

AS A GESTURE OF GOODWILL I WOULD LIKE TO INVITE YOU TO MY HUMBLE ABODE FOR DINNER.

THAT'S VERY KIND I ACCEPT. SHOULD I BRING ANYTHING?

FOOD, WINE AND A COUPLE OF LOOSE WOMEN.

THIS LOOKS LIKE A GOOD SPOT TO HAVE DINNER.
1984

THIS ROCK WILL MAKE AN IDEAL TABLE.

LET ME SEE - IT'S SO LONG SINCE I ENTERTAINED THAT I'VE FORGOTTEN THE PROPER ETIQUETTE.

DOES ONE GET BLIND DRUNK TO THE LEFT OR THE RIGHT OF THE GUEST?

YOU'VE ARRIVED— SIT DOWN! SIT DOWN!
1985

I DIDN'T KNOW WHAT YOU'D BE SERVING SO I BROUGHT THIS VERSATILE LITTLE WINE.

IT'S DRY AND FRUITY AND SHOULD COMPLIMENT MOST DISHES.
BURP! IT WAS FINE.

I'M VERY PLEASED YOU INVITED ME TO DINNER.
1986

I'VE BEEN LOOKING FORWARD TO SAMPLING LOCAL AUTHENTIC DISHES COOKED TRADITIONALLY IN AN IRON POT!

GRUB UP! THE TOMATO SOUP'S BOILING!

WAS THAT IT?
WHAT?
1987

THE MEAL—WAS THAT IT? ONE CAN OF TOMATO SOUP?

OF COURSE THAT WASN'T IT! WHAT KIND OF HOST DO YOU THINK I AM?

THERE'S ANOTHER CAN OF IT HEATING RIGHT NOW!

I'M GOING! I'VE NEVER BEEN SO INSULTED!
1988

THE "DINNER" YOU INVITE ME TO TURNS OUT TO BE TWO CANS OF TOMATO SOUP AND **YOU** DRINK ALL THE WINE **I** BROUGHT!

THAT'S RIGHT— LEAVE ME WITH ALL THE WASHING-UP!

EVENING, PEEP!
ER...EVENING, COLONEL.
1977

I SUPPOSE YOU'RE WONDERING WHAT I'M DOING OUT HERE ON THE WALL AT 3A.M.?
WELL, YES...

SO AM I—I WAS LOOKING FOR THE TOILET.

LOOK AT THAT MOON, PEEP—MAGNIFICENT, ISN'T IT!
1978

IT ALWAYS REMINDS ME OF MY WIFE...

...SHE GOES WHITE LIKE THAT AFTER THREE BOTTLES OF SHERRY.

HAVE YOU EVER SEEN MY MEDALS, PEEP?
NO, SIR.
1979

ER...THAT'S A MILK-TOP, SIR.
THAT'S FOR BEING THE CREAM OF THE INFANTRY!

HAR-DE-HAR-HAR-HAR!

HOW DOES IT FEEL HAVING A FUN-GUY FOR A COLONEL?

AHA!
WHAT IS IT, COLONEL?
1980

OHO!
IS IT TROUBLE, SIR?

AHA-OHO!
WHAT IS IT?

FUNNY NOISES IN THE BACK OF MY THROAT.

I KNOW YOU THINK I'M A BIT DOTTLED AT TIMES, PEEP...
1981

...BUT BELIEVE ME, THIS OLD BRAIN IS AS SHARP AS EVER!
YES, SIR.

LET'S SEE YOUR BELLY-BUTTON.

I ENJOY OUR CHATS, PEEP.
1982

IT GIVES ME A PICTURE OF THE COMMON SOLDIER.

AND, MY GOD, BUT YOU'RE UGLY.

THERE MUST BE SOME REASON WHY I'M A FAILURE.
2047

CHARM? I HAVE THAT. INTELLIGENCE? YEP. LOOKS, WIT, STYLE—I'VE GOT ALL THOSE.

THERE CAN ONLY BE ONE ANSWER...

...I UNDERESTIMATE MYSELF.

THIS IS A TIME FOR BRUTAL HONESTY.
2048

WHAT CHARACTERISTIC DO I LACK WHICH STOPS ME BEING SUCCESSFUL?

I'M STUCK AT "SCUFFED SANDALS."

I THINK I MAY HAVE FOUND THE REASON FOR MY FAILURE.
2049
WHAT WOULD I SAY TO SOMEONE THAT HEIGHT WHO WAS DEMANDING RANSOM MONEY?
"LOOK, A TALKING MUSHROOM."
I NEED TO MAKE MYSELF LOOK TALLER, MORE IMPOSING.
2050
MAYBE IF I SHORTEN MY ROBE, MY LEGS WILL LOOK LONGER.
MAYBE IF I SHORTEN MY ROBE, THEY'LL ALL DIE LAUGHING.

I'VE GOT IT! I KNOW HOW TO MAKE MYSELF LOOK TALLER!
CLICK!
2051

I'LL LENGTHEN MY ROBE AND WEAR STILTS UNDERNEATH!

HELP ME, PLEASE.

WHO NEEDS STILTS!
2052

I MIGHT NOT BE TALL... I MIGHT NOT EVEN BE MEDIUM... BUT AT LEAST I'M STUPID!

I MIGHT NOT BE TALL... I MIGHT NOT EVEN BE MEDIUM... BUT AT LEAST I'M STUPID!

HANG ON... I THINK I'M MISSING A "NOT" SOMEWHERE.

SIGH! MONDAY NIGHTS AT HOME.
2053

MY DORIS WILL PROBABLY BE DOWN THE CLUB HAVING A FEW DRINKS WITH THE REGULARS.

NO SHE WON'T— IT'S ELEVEN O'CLOCK SHE'LL BE OUTSIDE FIGHTING.

THE PEOPLE BACK HOME WILL BE DOING THEIR CHRISTMAS SHOPPING JUST NOW.
12054

SLIPPERS FOR GRANDADS, HANKIES FOR MUMS...

IT'S FUNNY HOW WE ALL BUY THE SAME THINGS.

I GOT MY GRANDAD A PADLOCK.

YOU'RE GIVING YOUR GRANDAD A PADLOCK FOR CHRISTMAS?
YES.
2055

DID HE ASK FOR ONE?
NO.

DOES HE WANT ONE?
I DON'T KNOW!
THEN WHY GET HIM ONE?
IT'S CHRISTMAS!

BEFORE YOU ASK, I'M WRITING MY CHRISTMAS LIST.
2056

AND, SINCE YOU CAN'T READ, YOU WON'T KNOW WHAT I'M GETTING YOU!

DO US A FAVOUR, SARGE— SHOW ME WHAT THE WORD "BIKE" LOOKS LIKE!

ARE YOU STILL WRITING YOUR CHRISTMAS LIST?
YES.
2057

DOES THAT SAY "DENNIS—A BIKE"?

NO, IT SAYS "DENNIS—A BRAIN TRANSPLANT."

JUST GIVE ME A TINY CLUE WHAT YOU'RE GETTING ME FOR CHRISTMAS.
2058

DOES IT HAVE HANDLEBARS, A BELL, A SEAT, WHEELS, A CHAIN, MUDGUARDS, TYRES, SPOKES AND PEDALS?
NOT UNLESS BARS OF CHOCOLATE HAVE TAKEN UP CYCLING.

NOW TO MAKE THE CHRISTMAS PUDDING... A TOUCH OF SHERRY...
GLUG
GLUG!
2059

...A TOUCH OF BRANDY...
GLUG!
GLUG!

...A TOUCH OF RUM...
GLUG!
GLUG!

NOW, WHERE DID I PUT THAT RAISIN?

WHAT CAN I DO TO MAKE THE TABLES LOOK MORE FESTIVE?

I KNOW! I COULD SCULPT LITTLE SNOWMEN FROM ICING SUGAR AND DECORATE THEM WITH CHOCOLATE EYES AND CANDY NOSES!
CLICK!

OR I COULD HAVE ANOTHER BOTTLE OF SHERRY.
2060

WHAT'S THAT?
A LITTLE SNOWMAN.
2061

I WANTED TO BRING A TOUCH OF CHRISTMAS TO YOUR TABLE...SOME FESTIVE CHEER.

THAT'S NICE, EGON - WHAT'S IT MADE FROM?

CAMEL DUNG.

ARE WE HAVING TURKEY FOR CHRISTMAS THIS YEAR?
2062

YES, BUT IT'S A VERY SMALL ONE.
HOW SMALL?

IT'S AN EGG.

I LIKE PREPARING CHRISTMAS DINNER.
CHOP! CHOP!
2063

IT'S THE LITTLE EXTRA TOUCHES THAT MAKE IT SPECIAL...
CHOP!

...LIKE PLACE-NAMES.
BEAU

WHAT ARE YOU DOING?
I'M GOING OVER MY CHRISTMAS DINNER CHECK-LIST.

TURKEY... POTATOES... VEGETABLES... PUDDING... YES, THEY'RE ALL HERE.

THAT'S WHAT I SWAPPED FOR THIS BOTTLE OF SHERRY!
2064

HERE'S YOUR CHRISTMAS PRESENT, BEAU.
2065

I THINK I CAN GUESS WHAT THIS IS!
YOU CAN?

WELL, YES-JUDGING BY THE SHAPE OF IT!
OH, I SEE— THE BOTTLE.

IT'S ALL I COULD FIND TO PUT THE HANKY IN.

LOOK WHAT MY MUM SENT ME FOR CHRISTMAS!
SUNGLASSES!

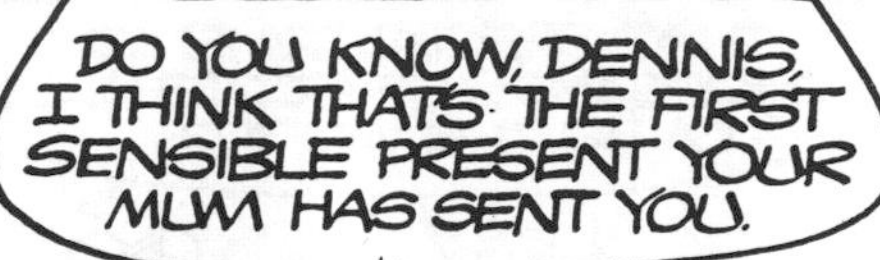
DO YOU KNOW, DENNIS, I THINK THAT'S THE FIRST SENSIBLE PRESENT YOUR MUM HAS SENT YOU.

2066

AND WHEN YOU TWIDDLE THIS KNOB HERE THEY PLAY "JINGLE BELLS."

I'M WEARING ALL THE CHRISTMAS PRESENTS FROM MY FAMILY.
2067

VERY TASTEFUL.
I THINK SO!

IT'S A PITY YOU CAN'T SEE THE UNDERPANTS FROM AUNT EDITH — THEY'VE GOT NAKED LADIES WITH BEACHBALLS ON THEM.

WELL, HAMISH, WE'RE GETTING CLOSE TO THAT SPECIAL TIME OF THE YEAR...
2068

...THAT SPECIAL TIME TO THOUSANDS OF SCOTS ALL OVER THE WORLD.

WHAT, OPENING TIME?

WELL, IT'S SOON HOGMANAY, HAMISH.
AYE.
2069

COULD YOU TEACH ME A SCOTTISH TOAST? SOMETHING YOU SAY AS YOU SIP YOUR LAST WHISKY OF THE YEAR?
"HELP ME UP."

THE NEW YEAR'S A SAD TIME FOR US EXILED SCOTS.
2070

YE CANNIE HELP THINKIN' ABOOT YOUR LOVED ONES AT HOME.

DIARY

WAIT A MINUTE. DUNDEE UNITED ARE NO AT HOME— THEY'RE AWAY!
DIARY

New Year Resolution—
I won't call Dennis stupid ever again.
2071

HAVE YOU DONE YOUR NEW YEAR REVOLUTION YET?

WHAT WAS THAT?
NOTHING.

MY NEW YEAR REVOLUTION IS—
RESOLUTION, DENNIS.
2072

MY NEW YEAR RESOLUTION IS TO BE MORE GENEROUS.

MY MISTAKE—THAT IS REVOLUTION.

AT LAST MY PARCEL HAS ARRIVED!
2073

THIS IS, WITHOUT DOUBT, MY BEST PLAN YET!

SLAUGHTER 'EM FROM THE INSIDE!

I, THE NOMAD, WILL POSE AS A NEW RECRUIT!

I HAVE STUDIED ALL THE MILITARY JARGON SO THAT I WILL REMAIN UNDETECTED.
2074

WHO GOES THERE?
ABLE SEAMAN SMITH REPORTING FOR DUTY, WING COMMANDER SIR!

MY DISGUISE IS PERFECT!
2075

ONCE I GAIN THEIR CONFIDENCE, I'LL BE ABLE TO SLAUGHTER 'EM.

I JUST HAVE TO AVOID MAKING SILLY MISTAKES.

WHAT ARE YOU DOING TONIGHT?
SLAUGHTERING YOU.

YOU LOOK FAMILIAR.
ME?
2076

NO, NO, NOT ME! I'M NOT FAMILIAR AT ALL! I'M UNFAMILIAR!

IF I WERE TO ASK YOU FOR TODAY'S PASSWORD, WHAT WOULD YOU SAY?

MUMMY.

DID YOU THINK YOU COULD FOOL US?
2077

YOU DON'T LOOK ANYTHING LIKE A LEGIONNAIRE.
I KNOW...

...DAMN THESE GOOD LOOKS!

I'M A FAILURE.
MY UNCLE USED TO SAY "SUCCESS IS LIKE A SCORPION BETWEEN THE EAGLE AND THE SULTANA."
2078

I'M A FAILURE WITH AN UNCLE WHO GIBBERS.

I'M ON SENTRY DUTY WITH MAD PIERRE.
ROTA
2079

WELL, THIS YEAR THINGS ARE GOING TO BE DIFFERENT.
ROTA

I'LL MEET HIS VIOLENCE WITH MY VIOLENCE!

I'LL BLEED ALL OVER HIS FISTS.

THAT'S BEEN MY TROUBLE— I'VE ALWAYS TRIED TO REASON WITH MAD PIERRE.
2080

A MAN LIKE HIM ONLY UNDERSTANDS VIOLENCE.

I'LL GAIN HIS RESPECT BY BEING TOUGH LIKE HIM!

HEY, BUDDY— LET'S EAT SHERBET BONBONS TILL WE'RE SICK!

I CAN SENSE MY NEW TOUGH IMAGE IS IMPRESSING PIERRE.
2081

WAIT TILL HE SEES ME LIGHT THIS MATCH ON MY TEETH!

WHAT HAPPENED TO YOU?
I SET FIRE TO MY MOUSTACHE.
SURGERY

IT'S WORKING! SINCE I ADOPTED MY NEW TOUGH GUY IMAGE, PIERRE HASN'T HIT ME ONCE!
2082

I'VE GOT TO KEEP IT UP— SHOW HIM I'M A FELLOW HARD-CASE!

LET'S PLAY BLIND MANS BUFF—WITHOUT THE BLINDFOLD.

I FEEL HUNGRY— GOT ANY BROKEN GLASS ?
2083

THAT'S IMPRESSED HIM. HE'S CONVINCED I'M A TOUGH GUY LIKE HIM!

WHY, DO YOU NEED IT TO MAKE NEW WINDOWS FOR YOUR DOLL'S HOUSE?

OKAY, SO I'M NOT A TOUGH GUY LIKE YOU!
2084

BUT I'D RATHER BE A SENSITIVE, CARING PERSON THAN A MINDLESS GORILLA.

WHACK!

THEN THERE ARE OTHER DAYS WHEN I WOULDN'T MIND.

I'VE BEEN THINKING, SERGEANT.
OH, NO.
2085

WHAT PRECAUTIONS HAVE WE TAKEN AGAINST THE SWISS ATTACKING THE FORT?
THE SWISS?

YES, SERGEANT, THE SWISS! THOSE WARMONGERS FROM SWITZERLAND!
ER... NONE SIR.

WHAT DO SLOPPY SERGEANTS LOSE?
STRIPES, SIR.

RIGHT, SERGEANT, WHERE DO YOU THINK THOSE SWISS MURDERERS WILL ATTACK FROM?
2086

SIR, I DON'T THINK SWITZERLAND HAS PLANS TO ATTACK ANYBODY.

THEY'RE NEUTRAL, SIR—THEY HAVEN'T FOUGHT A WAR IN CENTURIES.
I KNEW IT!

THEY'RE STOCKPILING ARMS!

KEEP YOUR EYES OPEN FOR THE SWISS TONIGHT!
THE SWISS?
2087

THEY DON'T FOOL ME, PEEP, WITH THEIR PEACEFUL MOUNTAINS, THEIR WATCHES AND THEIR CHEESE!

THEY'RE A BLOODTHIRSTY BUNCH!
THE SWISS?

KEEP THOSE BARBARIANS OUT AND THERE'S A GONG IN IT FOR YOU!
THE SWISS?

RIGHT, MEN, LINE UP FOR INSPECTION!
2088

AT LEAST THE COLONEL'S GOT OVER HIS CRAZY NOTION THAT SWITZERLAND IS ABOUT TO INVADE US!

ANYBODY — WHAT DO YOU DO IF A MAN FROM ZURICH ATTACKS YOU?

HOW'S THE COLONEL?
TOTALLY MAD.
2089

HE'S CONVINCED THAT BLOODTHIRSTY HOARDS FROM SWITZERLAND ARE ABOUT TO ATTACK THE FORT.

BLAM!

SORRY—I THOUGHT I HEARD A YODEL!

YOU'VE GOT TO SPEAK TO HIM, SARGE, HE'S TOTALLY MAD!
COLONEL ESCARGOT
2090

TELL HIM HE NEEDS SOME LEAVE. IF YOU'RE FIRM I'M SURE HE'LL SEE SOME SENSE!

SIR, CAN I BE FRANK...
COLONEL ESCARGOT
OH, GOODY! A GAME! LET'S SEE... I'LL BE WALTER!

CRACK!

'ALLO, BOYO! THE NAME'S LLANDUDNO JONES— I'M ON A QUEST TO FIND THE GOLDEN LADY OF MOROCCO!

2091
AREN'T WE ALL?

THE NAME'S LLANDUDNO JONES—ADVENTURER.

I TRAVEL THE WORLD IN SEARCH OF MISSING RARITIES.
2092

YOU HAVEN'T COME ACROSS A BRAIN, HAVE YOU?

IT MUST BE A GREAT LIFE BEING AN ADVENTURER!

THRILLS, BEAUTIFUL WOMEN, POTS OF MONEY!
IT HAS ITS DRAWBACKS...

CRACK!

...I'M DAMNED IF I CAN WORK THIS THING.
2093

WHAT'S THE MOST DIFFICULT QUEST YOU'VE BEEN ON, LLANDUDNO?

WELL, IT TOOK ME TWO YEARS TO FIND THE LOST COBRA OF KHARTOUM...

2094

...AND I'VE YET TO FIND MY LOST BUS-PASS OF CARDIFF.

FAREWELL, LLANDUDNO JONES!

SIGH! WHAT A LIFE, SEARCHING FOR LOST TREASURES!

THE WORLD IS YOUR DOMAIN, AND DANGER YOUR COMPANION.

2095
CAN I USE YOUR TOILET BEFORE I GO?

NOW TO CONTINUE WRITING MY BESTSELLER.

THAT LUSTY SAGA OF DESERT LIFE BROUGHT UP TO DATE.

"Sand in my Y Fronts II"
2096

WHAT CAN I CALL THE HERO OF MY BOOK?

SOMETHING RUGGED AND MASCULINE THAT REFLECTS THE HARDSHIP OF THE DESERT.

"The name's Bottom," he growled "Sandy Bottom."
2097

I MUST MAKE SURE MY BOOK IS A BESTSELLER.

LET'S SEE–IT HAS MYSTERY, ROMANCE, SEX AND VIOLENCE...

...GOT IT!

CHAPTER 4
Play 10 card Bingo.
2098

CHAPTER 5
He was 6 feet 4" and incredibly handsome.

He was the toughest man on earth and women adored him.

THIS IS EMBARASSING— THE READERS WILL SPOT IT'S ME RIGHT AWAY!
2099

THIS IS THE MOMENT ALL AUTHORS DREAD.
2100

THE LETTER FROM THE PUBLISHERS THAT COULD CHANGE HIS LIFE.

THEY HAVEN'T SENT MY BOOK BACK—THAT MUST BE A GOOD SIGN!

Dear Sir,
Your book was so awful we burned it.

EGON, I NEED YOUR HELP.

YOU KNOW HOW BEAU ALWAYS SAYS I'M STUPID?
YES.

WELL, I WANT YOU TO HELP ME PROVE HIM WRONG!
HANG ON, DENNIS, I CAN'T AFFORD TO BUY YOU A BRAIN TRANSPLANT.
2101

YOU SEE, I WANT TO SHOW BEAU THAT I'M NOT THICK.

I THOUGHT MAYBE YOU COULD TEACH ME ALL ABOUT SOME FAMOUS PERSON.

WHAT, YOU MEAN LIKE SHAKESPEARE OR SOMEONE?
EXACTLY!

TELL ME WHO HE PLAYED FOR, GOALS HE SCORED— EVERYTHING!

OKAY, DENNIS, WE'LL GIVE IT A TRY.

I'LL TEACH YOU ALL ABOUT A FAMOUS PERSON AND YOU CAN IMPRESS BEAU WITH YOUR KNOWLEDGE!

HORATIO NELSON!
BLESS YOU.
2103

OFF YOU GO, DENNIS—I'M SURE YOU'LL IMPRESS BEAU.

I'VE TAUGHT YOU EVERYTHING THERE IS TO KNOW ABOUT HORATIO NELSON.
AND REMEMBER—TRY TO BRING UP THE SUBJECT CASUALLY. BE SUBTLE.

YOU LOOK LIKE REAR-ADMIRAL HORATIO NELSON!
2104

I'LL IMPRESS BEAU WITH ALL THE STUFF EGON TAUGHT ME ABOUT NELSON!

WHEN WAS NELSON BORN, SMARTIE?
HORATIO? 1758. HE BECAME REAR-ADMIRAL AFTER THE BATTLE OF CAPE ST. VINCENT IN 1797.

2105
WHY DID YOU BREAK MY GLASSES, DENNIS?

I'M SITTING MY SERGEANT'S EXAM AGAIN TODAY.

I'VE ALWAYS FAILED BECAUSE I WAS TOO TENSE.

THIS TIME, I'M GOING TO HAVE A TINY DRINK JUST TO RELAX ME.

2106
LET'S GET THIS ©!!☠*!!☆ SHOW ON THE ROAD, BIG BOY!

WHAT'S THE MATTER WITH PEEP?
QUIET. SERGEANT'S EXAM IN PROGRESS.

HE WAS NERVOUS— HE SAID HE WAS GOING TO HAVE A GLASS OF WINE TO RELAX.

THE EXAMINER WANTS MY NAME — WHAT IS IT?
2107

I'M GLAD I HAD A LITTLE DRINK BEFORE MY EXAM.

IT'S HELPED ME TO RELAX AND THINK RATIONALLY.

SERGEANT'S EXAM:-
HOW WOULD YOU PUNISH A MAN INCORRECTLY DRESSED ON PARADE?
2108

Boil him in Oil.

SERGEANT'S EXAM:—
YOU ARE ABOUT TO ADVANCE ON AN ENEMY CAMP IN DARKNESS.

WHAT IS THE CORRECT ORDER?

2109
A GIN AND TONIC!

OOOH—WHAT HAVE I DONE?

YOU GOT BLIND DRUNK BEFORE YOU SAT YOUR SERGEANT'S EXAM.

DID I PASS?
NO.

THE STRIPES?
2110
YOU PAINTED THEM ON DURING THE EXAM.

I USED TO LOVE THIS TIME OF YEAR AT HOME.

THE FIRST DAFFODILS... NEW-BORN LAMBS...
GUY FAWKES NIGHT.

2111
THAT'S YOUR RECORD— 28 STUPID REMARKS BEFORE BREAKFAST.

THERE'S SOMETHING SPECIAL ABOUT SPRING, DENNIS.

MOTHER NATURE RE-AWAKENS AFTER HER ANNUAL SLUMBER.
"BEHOLD!" SHE CRIES, "COME SEE MY SPLENDOUR!"

2112
AND YOU CALL ME DAFT.

ARTISTS FIND SPRING A GREAT INSPIRATION.

WOULD THAT THEY COULD *MATCH* THE COLOURS OF MOTHER NATURE'S PAINT-BOX.
2113

THEY COULD USE MY CRAYONS!
CLICK!

PARIS IN THE SPRING—THE CITY OF LOVERS.

SIGH!
IMAGINE WALKING HAND-IN-HAND ON THE BANKS OF THE SEINE.

IT'D BE EVEN BETTER IF WE TOOK GIRLS!
2114

WELL, THAT'S BEEN AN INTERESTING DISCUSSION, DENNIS.

I USED TO THINK YOU WERE AN INSENSITIVE HALF-WIT.

2115
IT JUST SHOWS YOU HOW RIGHT YOU CAN BE.

ANY CHANCE OF SOME FOOD, PAL?

"PAL" INDEED! YOU SPENT THE WHOLE OF LAST WEEK TRYING TO SHOOT ME!

2116
TYPICAL, ISN'T IT? WE ALWAYS HURT THE ONES WE LOVE.

STOP BEGGING FOR FOOD AND GO AWAY!

WHAT HAPPENED TO YOUR ONCE-PROUD NOMADIC RACE?

THOSE RELENTLESS HUNTERS WHO COULD TRACK WILD GAME ACROSS SAND AND ROCK!

2117
NOT ME – I COULDN'T FIND THE MEAT COUNTER IN TESCO'S.

GOT IT! THE PERFECT WAY TO GET FOOD!

I'LL GET MYSELF ARRESTED– THEY'LL FEED ME IN JAIL!

I'LL COMMIT A CRIME LIKE HITTING A LEGIONNAIRE...

...OR DROPPING LITTER.
2118

HERE YOU ARE- SOME CHICKEN SANDWICHES.

MY GRATITUDE KNOWS NO BOUNDS, MY FRIEND—MY HEART IS FILLED.

WHICH IS MORE THAN THESE SANDWICHES ARE, YOU MEAN, FOUR-EYED GIT.
2119

D'YOU WANT TO HELP ME WITH THIS JIGSAW-PUZZLE, BEAU?

DENNIS, I PREFER TO SPEND MY SPARE TIME WITH SOMETHING LESS CHILDISH.

IT'S A NAKED LADY!

2120
FIND THE STRAIGHT BITS FIRST!

THIS JIGSAW'S QUITE DIFFICULT.

ARE YOU SURE IT'S A NAKED LADY?
YEP!

SHOULD SHE HAVE THREE OF THOSE?
2121

JIGSAWS REQUIRE PATIENCE, DENNIS.
THUMP!

IT'S A NAKED LADY! I WANT TO SEE WHAT SHE LOOKS LIKE!
THUMP!

2122
JUDGING BY THE BOX SHE SPENDS MOST OF HER TIME TOPPLING OVER.

PLEASE FIT!
JUST LOOK AT YOURSELF, DENNIS.

ONE NAKED LADY JIGSAW AND YOU GO BERSERK— JUST RELAX AND THINK.
PUFF! PUFF!

2123
I'LL GET A MALLET!
CLICK!

THERE ARE TWO BITS MISSING!

A NAKED LADY JIGSAW WITH TWO BITS MISSING!

A NAKED LADY JIGSAW WITH TWO BIG, IMPORTANT BITS MISSING!
2124

HE'S SLEEPING NOW— A COUPLE OF DAYS REST SHOULD SEE HIM OKAY.
INFIRMARY

IT AFFECTS MY NERVES, DOCTOR.

EVERY TIME I WORK WITH MAD PIERRE HE HITS ME!

RIGHT— TAKE THIS!
RIP!

2125
"COVER."

ARE THESE TRANQUILLISERS?
YES.
WOULD THEY, SAY, MAKE A VIOLENT MAN MORE PEACEFUL?
OH, ABSOLUTELY — CALM HIM RIGHT DOWN.

2126
COFFEE, PIERRE?

THIS COFFEE TASTES FUNNY.

IT'S WORKING! THE TRANQUILLISERS WILL STOP HIM HITTING ME!

WACK!

I HATE FUNNY-TASTING COFFEE!
2127

I FEEL DROWSY.

I'M NOT SURPRISED, SUCKER! I DRUGGED YOUR COFFEE TO WEAKEN YOU!

WACK!

IT'S WORKING! MY NOSE ONLY BROKE IN ONE PLACE!
2128

WHAT A GENIUS I AM... I DOPED MAD PIERRE'S COFFEE SO HE'S TOO TIRED TO HIT ME...
ZZZZZ

...AND I'M SO HAPPY I FINISH HIS COFFEE.
ZZZZZZ

2129
ZZZZZZZ
ZZZZZ

LOOK WHAT I BOUGHT AT THE PET SHOP BEAU!
A GOLDFISH! AT LEAST THEY DIDN'T CON YOU THIS TIME!

2130
IT'S NOT A DOLPHIN, THEN?

WHAT'S YOUR GOLDFISH CALLED?
ANN!

ANN? WHAT KIND OF NAME IS THAT FOR A FISH?

2131
A FIRST NAME.

BEAU, SHE'S BLOWN A BUBBLE!
ANOTHER ONE! LOOK AT THIS— TWO AT ONCE!

D'YOU THINK SHE CAN DO THREE AT ONCE?

I'VE NO IDEA— I'M TOO EXCITED TO THINK.
2132

WATCH THIS, BEAU!

WHAT'S TWO AND TWO, ANN?

LOOK — FIVE BUBBLES! SHE'S AS CLEVER AS ME!

2133
YOU COULD BE BROTHER AND SISTER.

ANN THE GOLDFISH IS DEAD.

I'M SORRY, DENNIS, BUT GOLDFISH ARE NOTORIOUS FOR THAT.

DID YOU FIND HER FLOATING IN HER BOWL?

2134
NO, TIED UP OUTSIDE THE PUB WHERE I LEFT HER.

I WANT A WORD WITH YOU, ABDUL!
HONEST ABDUL
1976

STOP CHEATING MY MATES OUT OF MONEY! WE'RE NOT ALL STUPID, YOU KNOW!

IT WAS A SNIP— APPARENTLY WOMEN CAN'T RESIST IT!

WELL, THANK YOU VERY MUCH, DENNIS.
2028

I THOUGHT I WAS IN FOR ANOTHER BORING OLD NIGHT IN THE PUB.

BUT, YET AGAIN, THAT QUICKSILVER BRAIN OF YOURS CAME UP WITH ANOTHER FASCINATING DIVERSION!

I NEVER KNEW YOU COULD PLAY TUNES ON A PENCIL STUCK UP YOUR NOSTRIL.

WHERE DO YOU WANT TO GO ON OUR DAY OFF, DENNIS?
2024

THERE'S AN EXHIBITION OF NORTH AFRICAN ART IN TOWN...

...OR THE MUSEUM IS DISPLAYING SOME NEW ARCHAEOLOGICAL FINDS...
...OR THERE'S THE PUB AGAIN.

WHAT A WASTE OF A DAY OFF...
2025

...SITTING IN A DARK, DINGY PUB DRINKING WINE.
YOU'RE RIGHT...

...LET'S HAVE SOME BEER AS WELL!

THAT WAS DELICIOUS...
2029

...BUT SOMEHOW THE MEAL SEEMS INCOMPLETE.

...IT'S A PITY I NEVER FIND A DEAD GOAT WHICH WAS CARRYING A BOTTLE OF BRANDY AND A CIGAR.

IT'S A STRANGE LIFE WHEN YOU LOOK AT IT.
2030

QUITE MORBID, REALLY— NOT MANY LAUGHS IN THE CIRCLES I MOVE IN.

DEAD GOATS DON'T TELL "KNOCK-KNOCK" JOKES.

I SUPPOSE I'D BETTER GO AND WHEEL AROUND FOR A BIT...
2031

...JUST TO CHECK IN CASE ANY SNAKES, LIZARDS OR MICE HAVE SNUFFED IT.

IT'S A GREAT SHAME THAT BACON SARNIES DON'T DIE AROUND THESE PARTS.

OH, NO- IT'S THE WOULD-BE INTELLECTUAL.

IT'S A STRANGE THING BEING CLOSE TO YOU...
HERE WE GO.

KNOWING THAT IF I DIED, YOU'D STRIP ME TO THE BONE.
2032

PERSONALLY, I'M TEMPTED TO START RIGHT NOW.

I WONDER WHAT YOU THINK OF ME?
2033

NOT JUST ME, MANKIND IN GENERAL.

DO WE INSPIRE FEAR? HATRED? WONDER? HORROR?

ZZZZZZZ

IT'S A CHILLING FEELING LOOKING AT THOSE EYES.
2034

I DON'T KNOW WHY, BUT IT'S A COLD, CREEPING SENSATION.

I DO—YOUR FLIES ARE OPEN.

THIS WEEK WE WILL BE CONCENTRATING ON UNARMED COMBAT.

YOU WILL LEARN HOW TO COPE WITH A FULLY-ARMED OPPONENT.
2001

YOU WILL BE INTRODUCED TO MARTIAL ARTS...
HOWDY, MARSHAL!
VERY FUNNY, PEEP. 100 PRESS-UPS.

I WANT TO DISCUSS UNARMED COMBAT.
2002

HOW WOULD YOU RENDER A MAN HELPLESS ONLY USING ONE FINGER?

PRESS THE STARTER ON A STEAM-ROLLER AND FLATTEN HIM!
200 PRESS-UPS, PEEP.

WHAT DO YOU KNOW ABOUT THE MARTIAL ARTS, PEEP?
EVERYTHING!
2003

AIEEE! YAAAH!

THIS BODY IS A WEAPON!

I AGREE—A PEA-SHOOTER.

SELF-DEFENCE IS ALL ABOUT REFLEXES.
2004

I WILL TRY, VERY SLOWLY AT FIRST, TO HIT YOU WITH THIS STICK. YOU STOP ME.

OUCH!
BOP!

BRILLIANT, PEEP—WE'LL HAVE TO START CALLING YOU "THE CAT."

RIGHT, PEEP, TRY TO GRAB MY WRIST BEFORE I STAB YOU!
2005
HA-HAR!

I WAS LIKE A PANTHER! A BLUR OF ACTION!

I THINK I'LL STAB HIM AND SAY IT WAS AN ACCIDENT.

YOU'RE HOPELESS AT SELF-DEFENCE, PEEP!
BOP!
2006

IT'S YOUR REFLEXES—THEY'RE VIRTUALLY NON-EXISTENT! THE SLOWEST I'VE EVER SEEN!
OUCH!

I'LL JUST GO OVER MY PLANS FOR TAKING THE FORT ONCE MORE.
2012

I WANT TO MAKE SURE THERE ARE NO SNAGS.

I MOVE UP AT FIRST LIGHT THEN —DAMN!

I DON'T HAVE AN AIRFORCE!

THIS IS A BRILLIANT IDEA! I'LL PLAY ON THEIR SYMPATHY!
2013

WHEN THEY SEE ME LYING HERE, THEY'LL FEEL SORRY FOR ME AND TAKE ME IN!

QUICK, FIND SOME PEBBLES AND WE'LL SEE IF WE CAN HIT HIM!

MY BRILLIANT PLAN WON'T TAKE LONG TO WORK NOW!
2014

THE GATE! THEY'RE COMING TO TAKE ME IN!
CLICK! CLICK!

RUMBLE!

THE UNDERSIDE OF A CAMEL IS NOT THE PRETTIEST SIGHT I'VE EVER SEEN.

HERE COMES SOMEONE NOW!
2015

I'LL BE TAKEN TO THEIR MEDICAL ROOM AND THEN I'LL TAKE A HOSTAGE!

NEXT I CAN TAKE OVER THE FORT AND DEMAND LOTS OF CONDITIONS AND MONEY AND THINGS!

OR I COULD JUST LIE HERE.

I'VE COME OUT TO TELL YOU YOU'RE WASTING YOUR TIME.
2016

WE KNOW YOU'RE FAKING. YOU'RE NOT ILL AND WE WON'T TAKE YOU INSIDE SO THAT YOU CAN ATTEMPT TO SLAUGHTER US.

ANY CHANCE OF A CUPPA TEA?

DON'T EVER SLEEP AT NIGHT, BEAU PEEP!

DON'T EVER RELAX BECAUSE I'LL BE WAITING! SOMEWHERE, SOMETIME I'LL GET YOU!
2017

AND WHEN THAT TIME COMES YOU'LL BE FOUND WITH A SLIT THROAT!

THAT REMINDS ME. ANY CHANCE OF BORROWING A TIE? I'VE A PARTY TOMORROW.

APPARENTLY EGON'S ON HOLIDAY THIS WEEK.
1995

HIS SISTER IS GOING TO HELP HIM OUT.
GREAT!

DO YOU THINK SHE'LL BE SMALL AND PRETTY WITH BLUE EYES?

NO.

SO YOU'RE EGON'S SISTER?
YES.
1996

MY NAME'S BEAU. WHAT DO PEOPLE CALL YOU?

A ROTTEN COOK.
FLICK!

IT'LL BE NICE TO HAVE THE FEMININE TOUCH IN THE KITCHEN.
WHO ORDERED STEW?
I DID.
1997

SLAP!

WELL, SAY PLEASE NEXT TIME.

DID YOUR BROTHER TEACH YOU TO COOK?

YES, EGON GAVE ME LOTS OF HANDY HINTS.
1998

D'YOU KNOW HOW TO MAKE PASTRY LIGHT AND FLUFFY?
NO.

PITY. EGON HADN'T A CLUE EITHER.

WHAT'S THIS? I ASKED FOR FRIED EGGS!
1999

THEY ARE FRIED!
BUT THEY'VE STILL GOT THEIR SHELLS ON!

LISTEN, MATE, IF YOU WANT FANCY FOREIGN COOKING YOU CAN EAT ELSEWHERE!

IT'S AMAZING HOW ALIKE YOU AND EGON ARE.
YES, GOOD LOOKS RUN IN OUR FAMILY.
2000

HAR-HAR-HAR! HAR-DE-HAR! HAR-HAR!

SHE USES A LADLE JUST LIKE HER BROTHER, TOO.

ADMIT IT, DENNIS, —YOU DID IT!
I DID NOT!
2018

HONESTLY, DENNIS, YOU'RE SO CHILDISH!
I'M NOT!

I SUPPOSE SAILOR SAM BROKE HIS OWN HEAD OFF?

ARE WE GOING TO PLAY WITH YOUR BOAT NOW?
PLAY? PLAY?
2019

WE'RE NOT "PLAYING" DENNIS—WE'RE CONDUCTING EXPERIMENTS ON THE STREAMLINING OF OUR VESSEL!

BAGS I BE NELSON—YOU CAN BE DRAKE!

WILL YOU DO ME A FAVOUR, BEAU?
WHAT?
2020

WILL YOU NAME THE BOAT AFTER ME?

I'M AFRAID BOATS ARE FEMININE, DENNIS.

"HADDOCK-BRAIN" IS MASCULINE.

I'LL SEE HOW SHE SITS ON THE WATER FIRST.
2021

I MAY HAVE TO SHAVE A TINY FRACTION OFF THE STARBOARD SIDE FOR BALANCE.

GLOOP!

OR I MIGHT HAVE TO ADD A PERISCOPE AND CALL IT A SUBMARINE.

YOU CAN BE THE WIND, DENNIS.
2022

COME ON, DENNIS, BLOW IT TO THE SIDE!
PHHH!

PORT, DENNIS, PORT!
PHHH!

THIS IS A HELL OF A TIME TO START ORDERING DRINKS!
OPP

AN INTRICATE PIECE OF ENGINEERING RUINED BY **YOU**!

I SHOULD HAVE KNOWN YOU LACK THE MATURITY OF SUCH MATTERS!

IT JUST MEANS YOU DON'T GET TO PLAY WITH MY BOAT AGAIN!
2023

IT'S TIME I SORTED MYSELF OUT.

DAY AFTER DAY I LIE AGAINST THIS ROCK.

I THINK I'LL BUY A PILLOW.
2135

IT'S TIME I FACED UP TO THE FACTS.

I'M A LAZY, GOOD-FOR-NOTHING LAYABOUT!

DEAR ME, SHOUTING DOESN'T HALF EXHAUST YOU.
2136

WHY DO I LIE AROUND ALL DAY?

MAYBE I SHOULD DO SOME EXERCISES.

WIGGLE!

PANT! I'M GOING TO BE AS STIFF AS HELL IN THE MORNING.
2137

THIS LAZING AROUND HAS GOT TO STOP.

I'M GOING TO EXERCISE ONE PART OF MY BODY EVERY DAY.

I THINK I'LL DO MY HAIR TODAY.
2138

DAY TWO OF MY NEW FITNESS REGIME.

WIGGLE! WIGGLE!

WIGGLE! WIGGLE! WIGGLE!

PANT! IT'LL BE EASIER NOW I'VE GONE THROUGH THE PAIN BARRIER.
2139

SOMETIMES MY HAND GOES RED AND SOMETIMES MY KNEE.
2140

IT'S STRESS.

AT TIMES OF STRESS, BLOOD RUSHES TO THE BRAIN.

IN YOUR CASE IT RUSHES ROUND LOOKING FOR IT.

I KNOW WHAT WE'LL DO— TWENTY QUESTIONS!

I THINK OF SOMEONE FAMOUS AND YOU TRY TO FIND OUT WHO IT IS.

RIGHT—I'VE GOT ONE. ASK AWAY.

WHO IS IT?
2141

TIME UP, DENNIS— THE ANSWER WAS CLEOPATRA.

SHE WAS QUEEN OF EGYPT.

I KNOW WHO SHE WAS—I'M NOT STUPID!

SHE WAS BITTEN BY AN ASPIRIN!
2142

THIS IS A TOUGH ONE, DENNIS.
A LIVING AMERICAN SPORTSMAN? NO, I GIVE UP.
LITTLE MISS MOFFAT.
2143
THE MOMENT HAS FINALLY COME FOR ME TO BAYONET YOU, DENNIS.

ARE WE PLAYING TWENTY QUESTIONS TODAY, BEAU?

I DON'T THINK SO, DENNIS.

THE GAME SHOULD BE PLAYED BETWEEN SIMILAR INTELLECTS.

2144
PERHAPS YOU COULD BORROW A TIN OF CORNED BEEF.

A LETTER FROM MY DORIS.

Dear Beau,
Do you still remember my ruby lips?

YES I DO.

LIKE TWO RED SLUGS FIGHTING ON A PLATE OF PORRIDGE.
2145

I often think of us together in that little pub.

When I pass it now, I can't help shedding a quiet tear.

IT'S FUNNY BUT MY DORIS CAN BE QUITE SENSITIVE AT TIMES.

So I've Had "PIG AND WHISTLE" tattooed on my forehead.
2146

I remember, Darling Beau, how we played those silly lovers' games.

We skipped stones across the water.

Well, I did, You cut your finger on one, fainted, fell in the water and I carried you home.
2147

I have this Secret dream, Darling Beau...

...that one day I'll disguise myself as a man and join you in the Legion.
2148

JUST PROMISE ME, SARGE, IF YOU SEE ANYTHING LOOKING VAGUELY LIKE THIS PHOTO, SHOOT IT!

IS THAT A LETTER FROM YOUR DORIS?
YEP.

SHE'S DETERMINED TO GET HER HOOKS INTO ME.
HOW D'YOU KNOW?

2149
SHE'S BUILDING A WEDDING DRESS.

GUESS WHAT, BEAU!
WHAT?

IT'S AMATEUR NIGHT IN THE PUB TONIGHT!

2150
THEY WANT TO FIND NEW TALENT!
TAP! TAP! TAP!

AND THEY'RE LOOKING FOR HIPPO IMPRESSIONS, ARE THEY?

COO! I'M EXCITED!
BAR
TONIGHT AMATEUR NIGHT
2151
HAVE YOU GOT A STAGE NAME?
YEP!
"BIG, HANDSOME DENNIS THE BRILLIANT BLOKE."
BAR
CATCHY.

HAVE YOU GOT YOUR ACT WORKED OUT?
YEP!
TONIGHT AMATEUR NIGHT
I'M GOING TO DO MY FARMYARD ANIMAL NOISES— I'M BRILLIANT!
D'YOU MEAN LIKE A COW OR SOMETHING?
2152
HERE, THAT WOULD BE A GOOD ONE! WHAT DO THEY DO?

HERE COMES DENNIS'S FIRST ATTEMPT AT SHOWBIZ!
TONIGHT AMATEUR NIGHT

I SAY! I SAY! I SAY! MY DOG HAS NO NOSE— HOW DOES HE SMELL?
2153

BECAUSE THE CHICKEN CROSSED THE ROAD! *HAR! HAR! HAR!*
THERE GOES HIS LAST ATTEMPT AT SHOWBIZ.

DON'T BE DOWNHEARTED, DENNIS.
TONIGHT AMATEUR NIGHT

LOTS OF FAMOUS STARS FAILED TO BEGIN WITH!

2154
THOUGH, I'LL GRANT YOU, NOT MANY GET SHOT AT BY THE BAND.

ARE WE LOST, BEAU?

2155
DENNIS, WE HAVE THE SUN'S POSITION, A COMPASS, A MAP AND A WHISTLE.

WHAT'S THE WHISTLE FOR?
TO BLOW FOR HELP— WE'RE LOST.

MAP READING CAN'T BE *THAT* DIFFICULT.

THINK, DENNIS— WHAT DID THEY TEACH US?

DON'T YOU REMEMBER ALL THOSE LESSONS ABOUT LONGITUDE AND LATITUDE?

2156
YES. I HAD TO CLEAN THE BLACKBOARD.

MAYBE WE COULD SEND UP A ROCKET!
A ROCKET?
2157

AND DO YOU HAPPEN TO HAVE A ROCKET ON YOUR PERSON?
NO.

THAT'S A GREAT PITY, DENNIS...

...BECAUSE I KNEW EXACTLY WHERE I WAS GOING TO STICK IT.

WELL, DENNIS OL' BUDDY, THIS COULD BE IT.

WE'RE LOST, OUT OF WATER AND GOODNESS KNOWS WHEN OUR MINDS WILL GO.

2158
IF THERE'S ONE THING I HATE, IT'S A HADDOCK WHO CHEATS AT DOMINOES!

HEADS AGAIN-
DAMMIT!

MAKE IT BEST OF
A HUNDRED?
BETTER
NOT, SARGE.

2159
OH, ALL RIGHT-
WE'LL RESCUE
THEM!

YET ANOTHER
BRILLIANT IDEA-
PAINT MYSELF
BLACK!

THEN I WAIT UNTIL DARK
AND SNEAK INTO THE FORT!
I WONDER WHAT TIME
IT IS NOW?

AHA! BLACK
MINUTES TO
BLACK!
2160

AT LAST—THE SUN HAS GONE DOWN!
NOW, THANKS TO MY BRILLIANT BLACK PAINT CAMOUFLAGE, NOBODY WILL SEE ME!

RUMBLE! RUMBLE! RUMBLE!

NOT EVEN PASSING CAMELS.
2161

MY CUNNING BLACK PAINT DISGUISE HAS ALLOWED ME TO SNEAK UP TO THE FORT!
OH-OH, A SUSPICIOUS SENTRY! I'LL DO ONE OF MY BRILLIANT BIRD IMPRESSIONS!

COCK-A-DOODLE DOO!

HANG ON—THAT'S THE WRONG ONE! I MEANT "TU-WHIT TU-WOO!"
2162

WHEN YOU THINK ABOUT IT, THE NOMAD'S PLAN WAS QUITE BRILLIANT...

...TO PAINT HIMSELF BLACK THEN ATTACK THE FORT AT NIGHT.

THOUGH HE SHOULD HAVE WAITED TILL THE PAINT DRIED BEFORE CLIMBING THE WALL.
2163

SIGH! FAILED AGAIN!
FIDDLE!
SPAZ

WHY DO I LURCH FROM ONE DISASTER TO ANOTHER?

WHY HAS THE SCORPION THAT WAS UNDER THIS STONE JUST RUN UP MY SLEEVE?
2164

PEACE, PERFECT PEACE!
I'VE BEEN LOOKING FORWARD TO THIS—A GREAT AFTERNOON'S PAINTING.
SIGH! IT'S SO NICE TO GET AWAY FROM THE HUSTLE AND VULGARITY OF THE FORT.
HI, BEAU! I'LL BUY YOU A PINT IF YOU DRAW A NAKED LADY!
2165

DENNIS, I'VE GOT A BRILLIANT IDEA!

I'LL CAPTURE YOU ON CANVAS! WILL YOU SIT FOR ME?

WHY—WHERE ARE YOU GOING?
2166

I WANT TO TRY AND CAPTURE YOUR EXPRESSION, DENNIS.

2167
I THINK I'VE GOT IT ALREADY.

ARE YOU NEARLY FINISHED?
DENNIS, YOU CAN'T HURRY ART – IT'S ALL ABOUT CREATIVE FLOW.

I HAVE TO *FEEL* THE MOOD, GET THE EMOTION INTO MY PAINT.

2168
BESIDES, I'VE LOST MY PENCIL.

THAT'S IT! I'VE HAD ENOUGH OF POSING!

LET'S SEE WHAT YOU'VE DONE.

I'VE TRIED TO CAPTURE YOU AS YOU REALLY ARE.

2169
WHAT IS IT ?
A POTATO.

OH, NO—WE'VE GOT TO RUN A MARATHON!
NOTICES
WHAT'S THAT ?

YOU DON'T KNOW WHAT A MARATHON IS ?
NO.

2170
DO YOU KNOW WHAT DEATH IS ?

ARE YOU READY, DENNIS?
YES.
START

AHEAD OF US LIE 26 MILES OF HARD RUNNING.

I'LL SET MY WATCH SO WE CAN CHECK OUR TIME.

2171
THIS IS TUESDAY, ISN'T IT?

PUFF! I'VE HIT "THE WALL."
WHAT'S THAT?

IT'S WHAT HAPPENS TO ALL MARATHON RUNNERS AT SOME STAGE OF THE RACE.

ALTHOUGH I THOUGHT IT MIGHT COME A BIT LATER.
START
2172

HOW LONG DID YOU SAY A MARATHON WAS, BEAU?
26 MILES.

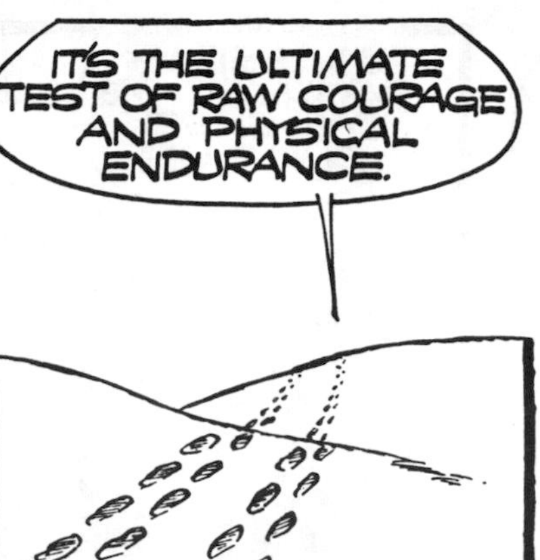
IT'S THE ULTIMATE TEST OF RAW COURAGE AND PHYSICAL ENDURANCE.

I'M GLAD WE DECIDED NOT TO BOTHER.
2173

HE'LL NEVER KNOW WE DIDN'T DO THE WHOLE MARATHON.
YEAH! IT WAS A GREAT IDEA TO HAVE A KIP INSTEAD.

JUST LOOK TIRED AND DON'T SAY ANYTHING STUPID.

SORRY WE'RE LATE — WE SLEPT IN.
2174

HEY, I KNOW WHAT WE CAN DO, DENNIS!

WE CAN HAVE A GAME OF FOOTIE!

2175
SLAP!

"FOOTIE," DENNIS— NOT "FOOTSIE."

I'M LOOKING FORWARD TO A KICKABOUT!

WHEN I WAS A KID, THEY USED TO CALL ME "THE WIZARD OF THE DRIBBLE"!

2176
I WAS A PRETTY SLOPPY EATER MYSELF.

HERE, TAKE THIS CHALK AND MARK A GOAL ON THE WALL.
I RECKON IF WE PRACTISE SERIOUSLY, WE COULD BE REALLY GOOD!
SHUFFLE!
YOU KNOW, STICK IN CONCENTRATE AND LEARN ALL THE GAMES BASICS.
JINK!
LOOK AT THIS DUCK I'VE DRAWN!
2177

DENNIS, WHAT ARE YOU DOING?
DIVING!

I REALISE THERE IS A CERTAIN AMOUNT OF ANTICIPATION IN A GOALIE'S JOB BUT YOU'VE GOT TO WAIT UNTIL I KICK IT TO YOU.

I'M NOT PLAYING WITH YOU — I JUST LIKE DIVING!
2178

IT'S GOOD TO ENCOURAGE SPORT.

IT TEACHES THE MEN DISCIPLINE AND HOW TO BE PART OF A TEAM — HOW TO BE *MEN*.

SERGEANT, HE CAN'T DRAW STRAIGHT LINES FOR THE GOAL AND HE WON'T GIVE ME THE CHALK!
2179

HALLO, HAMISH— HAVING A QUIET READ?
AYE.

AH, YES, QUITE A LITERARY TRADITION YOU SCOTS HAVE!

SIR WALTER SCOTT, ROBERT LOUIS STEVENSON, THE GREAT ROBERT BURNS...

WHAT ARE YOU READING?
A DUNDEE UNITED Vs. MORTON PROGRAMME.
2180

IS THAT WHISKY YOU'RE DRINKING, HAMISH?
AYE.

I'VE ALWAYS BEEN FASCINATED BY THAT STUFF.

WHAT'S THE DIFFERENCE BETWEEN MALT WHISKY AND ORDINARY WHISKY?

WELL, WI' MALT WHISKY YOU FALL TO THE LEFT...
2181

DID YE KEN THERE ARE OVER 2,000 DIFFERENT TYPES OF WHISKY?

2,000! GOODNESS, IT WOULD TAKE SOME TIME TO TRY OUT THAT LOT!

ELEVEN MONTHS TWO DAYS.
2182

LET'S HAVE A SING-SONG HAMISH!

DO YOU KNOW ANY SCOTTISH FOLK SONGS?
AYE!

THIS ONE'S CALLED "THE HEATHER'S 3 FEET HIGH."

THE CHORUS GOES "MY INSIDE LEG IS 2FT. 9." I CAN'T STOP LAUGHING, JIMMY."
2183

THAT WAS A GREAT NIGHT OUT, HAMISH!

I FEEL I'VE LEARNED A LOT ABOUT SCOTTISH CUSTOMS...

...LIKE THAT ONE WHERE I HAD TO BUY YOU A BOTTLE OF WHISKY WHEN YOU SNEEZED.
2184

WHAT ARE YOU DOING?
IT'S AN OLD CUSTOM...
...IF YOU WANT GOOD LUCK, TOUCH A TREE WITH YOUR ELBOWS. HAVE A GO.
THAT'S IT.
GOOD LUCK YOU SAY.
CLICK!
IT IS FOR ME.
2185

AT LAST I HAVE YOU, BEAU PEEP!

BUT I SHALL NOT GLOAT OVER YOUR HUMILIATION.

HERE, HOLD THIS WHILE I TAKE YOUR PICTURE.
2186
CAPTURED BY THE WORLD'S GREATEST MAN.

I'M ENJOYING THIS!

YOU'RE COMPLETELY UNDER MY CONTROL— I CAN DO ANYTHING I WANT!

...AND IN THIS ONE, I'M ON THE LEFT BESIDE MUM.
2187
PHOTO ALBUM

NOW, I'M SORRY TO HAVE TO BRING THE SUBJECT UP...

...BUT ABOUT YOUR DEATH —ANY PREFERENCES?

YES, DRUNK IN A HAREM, AGED 112.
2188

MAD PIERRE! THANK GOODNESS!

OH, HA-HA! PULL THE OTHER ONE, IT'S GOT BELLS ON!

WHACK!

2189
DING. DONG.

WHAT'S THE BOOK ABOUT?

POLITICS— YOU WOULDN'T UNDERSTAND.

WELL, THAT'S WHERE YOU'RE WRONG, SMARTY...

2190
...'COS I'VE EVEN MET OUR LOCAL M.C.!

TEACH ME TO READ AGAIN, BEAU!

I'LL TRY REALLY HARD THIS TIME! I'LL WORK NIGHT AND DAY!

OKAY, DENNIS— I'LL GO AND GET THE BOOK.

WHAT, NOW? OPENING TIME?
2191

RIGHT, DENNIS, WE'LL START AT THE BEGINNING
ABC

THERE ARE 26 LETTERS IN THE ALPHABET.
26!
ABC

WE'LL SOON CUT THAT DOWN IF WE GET RID OF THE CURLY ONES!
RIP
ABC
2192

...THERE... IS...JACK...
MY FIRST BOOK

...JACK...HAS ...A...CAT...
MY FIRST BOOK

...JACK... HAS...A... BIKE...
MY FIRST BOOK

JACK'S BEGINNING TO GET RIGHT UP MY NOSE!
MY FIRST BOOK
2193

I'M PROUD OF DENNIS.

HE'S WORKED VERY HARD AT HIS READING.

HE'S BEEN CONCENTRATING FOR HOURS ON THAT BOOK.

DONE IT! I'VE MANAGED TO GET MY PINKY UP THAT TUBE THING IN THE COVER!
2194

WELL, OUR ORDERS ARE QUITE SPECIFIC...

...SCOUT AND TRACK THE ENEMY FOR 48 HOURS.

WE'VE ALSO TO USE OUR INITIATIVE.

2195
WHAT DOES THAT MEAN?
WE HIDE FOR TWO DAYS.

YOU'VE GOT TO HAND IT TO THEM.
WHO?

MY SCHOOL-MATES. THEY WERE RIGHT.
2196

THEY ONCE VOTED ME "*THE BOY MOST LIKELY TO BE SCARED OF THE DARK.*"

SHHH! I THINK I HEARD SOMETHING!

QUICK—COVER THE FIRE WITH YOUR JACKET!
2197

DID I TELL YOU I SPILLED SOME PETROL ON MY JACKET?

LOOK, BEAU—THE ENEMY!

WHEN THE GOING GETS TOUGH, DENNIS, THE TOUGH GET GOING!
CLICK!

LET'S GET GOING!
2198

IT'S INTERESTING HOW PEOPLE REACT IN THE FACE OF DANGER.

THERE WE WERE, WITHIN A HUNDRED YARDS OF THE ENEMY.

I SCREAMED!
I SORT OF WHIMPERED!
2199

I'VE GOOD NEWS FOR YOU, PEEP...

...I'M MAKING YOU HEAD OF THE CAMEL CORPS.
THANK YOU, SIR!

UNLESS YOU'D PREFER TO BE THE REAR END ?
2200

THAT'S BRILLIANT, MEN!

HANG ON, WHICH OF YOU HAS THE HUMP?

WELL, NEITHER OF US IS VERY HAPPY, SIR.
2201

I THINK WE STILL LACK A BIT OF REALISM, PEEP.

MAYBE YOU SHOULD TRY MAKING A FEW CAMEL NOISES.

MOST OF THE ONES I'VE HEARD COME FROM THE OTHER END.
2202

...AND YOU'LL BE ABLE TO SPY IN THE ENEMY CAMP.

VERY GOOD IDEA, SIR. WHAT'S THAT BEHIND YOU?

2203
HERE, BEAU, YOU CAN'T DO THAT!

THIS WON'T WORK. YOU DON'T LOOK LIKE A CAMEL...

...YOU DON'T MOVE LIKE A CAMEL, SOUND LIKE A CAMEL...

2204
GOOD TH —
SILENCE THAT CAMEL! A WEEK WITHOUT HAY!

I DON'T BELIEVE THIS.

PLEASE LET THE APPROACHING FIGURE BE A MIRAGE.

HOWDY—THE NAME'S HANK TUMBLEWEED!
2205

I'VE DECIDED TO BECOME A COUNTRY AND WESTERN SINGER.

BY THE WAY, I'M NOW KNOWN AS HANK TUMBLEWEED...

...JUST IN CASE YOU HAVE TO WRITE A CHEQUE FOR MY FIRST ALBUM.
2206

LISTEN TO THIS SONG I'VE WRITTEN.
IT'S ABOUT A COWBOY WHO IS WRONGLY JAILED WHEN HIS WIFE DIES IN A CAR CRASH.
IT'S CALLED "DEREK THE COWBOY WHO'S WRONGLY JAILED WHEN HIS WIFE DIES IN A CAR CRASH."
2207

OH, I'M A LONESOME COWBOY

HO-RO! PULL UP THE ANCHOR ME BOYOS

BIT OF AN EXPERIMENT THERE—"COUNTRY AND SHANTY"
2208

A DESERT NOMAD CALLED HANK TUMBLEWEED...
...WHO WANTS TO BE A COUNTRY AND WESTERN SINGER.
I'VE SEEN EVERYTHING NOW.
NOT QUITE.
2209

HERE IT COMES.
BAR

ER... GET THE DRINKS UP, BEAU. I'LL JUST BE A SECOND!

THAT'S A NEW ONE—BURYING YOUR PURSE.
2210.

A GOOD GLASS OF WINE, DENNIS.

IT MAKES ME APPRECIATE THE FINER THINGS IN LIFE.

IT MAKES ME GRATEFUL THAT I CAN ENJOY A LUXURY UNAVAILABLE TO MANY.

2211
IT MAKES ME BURP.

SIP!

I BET I CAN TELL WHERE THIS WINE COMES FROM!

OH, YES? BECOME AN EXPERT ON THE WORLD'S VINEYARDS, HAVE WE?

2212
IT'S FROM THE TOP SHELF – IT'S ALL HOT WHERE THE SUN'S BEEN ON IT!

YOU'LL LIKE THIS WINE, DENNIS.

IT'S OLDER THAN THE OTHERS. VERY DRY AND VERY EXPENSIVE.

2213
SIP!

IT COULD DO WITH A TOUCH OF LIME IN IT!

SNIFF!

ALL RIGHT! YOU'VE MADE YOUR POINT!
SNIFF!

2214
I *DO* CRY WHEN SOMEONE HOLDS MY WALLET!

I HEARD YOU WERE IN HERE, DENNIS. WHAT'S UP?

2215
IT'S A BIT EMBARASSING. IT'S TO DO WITH MY BOTTOM.

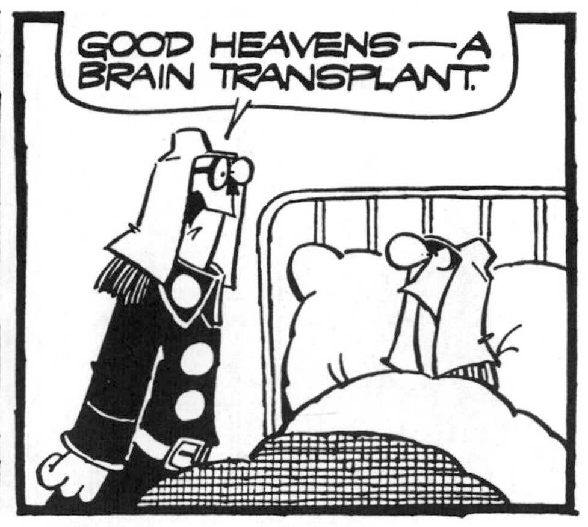
GOOD HEAVENS — A BRAIN TRANSPLANT.

ER... BEAU... YOU WON'T TELL THE LADS I'VE GOT A BOIL ON MY BOTTOM, WILL YOU?

WOULD I DO A THING LIKE THAT, DENNIS?

2216
INFIRMARY
THIS WAY TO SEE DENNIS'S BOIL, IT'S ON HIS BOTTOM

I'LL POP IN AND SEE HOW DENNIS IS.
INFIRMARY

AT TIMES LIKE THIS, THE THOUGHTFULNESS OF FRIENDS IS MUCH APPRECIATED.
INFIRMARY

2217
WHAT—NO GRAPES?

DO YOU THINK I'LL PULL THROUGH, BEAU?

2218
DENNIS, IT'S ONLY A SIMPLE BOIL ON YOUR BOTTOM!

UNLESS, OF COURSE, THE SCALPEL SLIPS AND DAMAGES YOUR BRAIN.

HOW'S DENNIS, DOC?
INFIRMARY

I'VE GIVEN HIM A SEDATIVE AND HE'S STILL A BIT DOPEY.

HOW CAN HE TELL?
2219

SCOTLAND MUST BE NICE AT THIS TIME OF YEAR, HAMISH.

MOUNTAINS... LOCHS... BONNIE PURPLE HEATHER...

SHE'S NO' THAT BONNIE — AND IT'S ONLY HER NOSE THAT'S PURPLE.
2222

IT'S FUNNY HOW YOU SCOTS GET ABOUT.

YOU COULD GO ANYWHERE IN THE WORLD AND YOU'D FIND A SCOTSMAN.

EXCEPT EDINBURGH.
2223

I'VE ALWAYS WANTED TO GO TO A SCOTTISH HIGHLAND GAMES.

WHAT'S THE NAME OF THAT BIG THING YOU THROW UP IN THE AIR?

A BARMAN.
2224

DO YOU HAVE HIGHLAND GAMES IN YOUR TOWN, HAMISH?
OH, AYE.

THERE'S PIPE BANDS, DANCING, ATHLETICS.

THAT MUST BE A REALLY COLOURFUL SIGHT.

AH'VE NAE IDEA — AH'VE NEVER GOT OUT O' THE BEER TENT.
2225

I ENJOYED OUR TALK ABOUT SCOTLAND, HAMISH.

YOU CERTAINLY DESTROYED SOME MYTHS — LIKE ALL SCOTS BEING MEAN.

WHAT'S THIS?
THE BILL FOR MY TALK.
2226

IT'S GREAT TO GET AWAY FROM THE FORT...

...AWAY FROM PEOPLE CALLING ME STUPID.

KEEP THE NOISE DOWN, DUMBO—SOME OF US ARE TRYING TO SLEEP!
2227

OKAY, DUMBO—WHAT'S YOUR PROBLEM?

THAT'S MY PROBLEM—EVERYONE CALLS ME STUPID AND I'M ***NOT***!

2228
OO! IT'S SO CASTRATING!

RIGHT—I'M GOING TO HELP YOU.

YOU WANT PEOPLE TO STOP CALLING YOU STUPID?
YES.

FIRST, BE POSITIVE. BE AN OPTIMIST.
2229

WHAT, TEST PEOPLE'S EYES?

I'VE GOT A PROBLEM TOO, YOU KNOW.

WHAT, BEING SHORT, FAT AND UGLY WITH NO FRIENDS?

2230

I WAS GOING TO SAY "*FIGHTING OFF WOMEN.*"

CAN I ASK YOU A QUESTION?
OKAY.
WHAT'S IT LIKE BEING DUMPY AND UGLY?
WELL, IT'S SORT OF—
WHAT'S IT LIKE BEING STUPID WITH A FAT LIP?
2231

WHAT'S THIS?

IT'S THE ADDRESS OF THAT USELESS LONELY HEARTS CLUB I WROTE TO.

2035

THOSE WOMEN ONLY WANT RICH, WELL-DRESSED, EDUCATED MEN!

OH, BOY—THIS IS FOR ME!
KITCHEN

Dear Lonely Hearts,

It's very difficult to write about oneself.
2036

Let's put it this way—one of your Birds is in for a treat.

Dear Lonely Hearts,
2037

I'm a quiet, practical man who would like to meet a quiet, practical woman.

on second thoughts, send me a raver by return.

Dear Lonely Hearts, I'll be honest.

I'm not the world's most handsome man.

2038

I'm about Fourth.

ALL I HAVE TO DO NOW IS ANSWER THE LONELY HEARTS QUESTIONNAIRE.
2039

It's Blue.

I LOVE "COLOUR OF EYES"!

MY REPLY FROM 'LONELY HEARTS'!
2040

DEAR SIR, I DO NOT THINK YOU HAVE UNDERSTOOD THE PURPOSE OF OUR CLUB.

NOT UNDERSTOOD? WHAT A CHEEK!

AND WHERE'S THE BOX WITH THE WOMAN I ORDERED?

DON'T YOU FEEL GUILTY, DENNIS.
WHY?
SPENDING OUR DAY OFF IN THE PUB WHEN WE COULD BE DOING SOMETHING ELSE.
LIKE WHAT?
I DON'T KNOW— VISITING PLACES OF INTEREST.
WHAT, LIKE A PUB CRAWL?
2026

YOU'RE QUIET, BEAU —WHAT ARE YOU THINKING ABOUT?
2027

NOTHING. ABSOLUTELY NOTHING. I'VE BEEN TRYING TO MAKE MY MIND A COMPLETE BLANK.

I WANT TO KNOW WHAT IT'S LIKE BEING YOU.

WOULDN'T IT BE GREAT TO BE FAMOUS?
2041

YOU KNOW, DO SOMETHING THAT WOULD BE REMEMBERED FOR EVER!

WHAT, LIKE YOU LIVING YOUR WHOLE LIFE WITHOUT A BRAIN?

BEAU, HOW SHOULD I GO ABOUT BECOMING FAMOUS?
2042
LET'S SEE—MOST FAMOUS PEOPLE ARE GREAT WRITERS OR COMPOSERS OR ARTISTS OR INVENTORS OR POLITICIANS.
WHAT CAN YOU DO?
COUNT TO EIGHT.

WHAT CAN I DO TO BECOME FAMOUS?
2043

I'VE GOT IT! I'LL BECOME A FILM STAR AND GET A LEADING ROLE!
CLICK!

I DOUBT IF HOLLYWOOD IS PLANNING A FILM ABOUT TREE-STUMPS.

IT'S PATHETIC, DENNIS– WHY ON EARTH DO YOU WANT TO BECOME FAMOUS?
2044

BECAUSE YOU GET LOTS OF MONEY AND WOMEN CHASE YOU ALL OVER THE PLACE!

MAYBE WE COULD WRITE A BEST-SELLER!

IF I BECOME FAMOUS I'LL GET A YACHT.
2045

AND I'LL GET A BIG HOUSE ON AN ISLAND!

DENNIS, TO BECOME FAMOUS YOU NEED INITIATIVE.

THEN I'LL BUY ONE— AND GET A CHAUFFEUR TO DRIVE IT!

SIGH! DENNIS AND HIS DREAMS!
2046

I SUPPOSE IT'S HEALTHY TO WANT TO REACH FOR THE STARS... TO HAVE AMBITION THAT WILL CATAPULT YOU AWAY FROM EVERYDAY LIFE.

I WONDER WHAT IT'S LIKE TO BE A BADGER?

BEAU, DO YOU KNOW ANY WORD GAMES WE COULD PLAY?
2010

DENNIS, YOUR VOCABULARY CONSISTS OF 34 WORDS, 23 OF WHICH ARE OBSCENE.

YOU THINK YOU'RE SMART, DON'T YOU? JUST BECAUSE YOU KNOW A FEW FANCY WORDS.
MY CONSTABULARY'S EVERY BIT AS GOOD AS YOURS!

JUST READ YOUR BOOK—I WON'T SAY ANOTHER WORD.
GOOD.
2011

I KNOW YOU LIKE PEACE AND QUIET SO I'LL SHUT UP.
FINE.

YOU WON'T KNOW I'M HERE. YOU WON'T HEAR A SINGLE SOUND FROM ME.

YOU FIRED 15 SHOTS.
I DIDN'T HIT HIM, THOUGH.